Footprints on the Page - Poetry R
by Charles Butchart with an introduction b

Contents

Introduction

WHY TEACH POETRY?

Poetry is an important part of any language curriculum. Good poems capture thoughts, feelings or experiences in moving or interesting ways. They might help children look at familiar things in a fresh light, explore emotions, or lodge ideas or insights in the memory. Whatever its particular effect, sharing a good poem is an enriching and satisfying experience.

There are other advantages to sharing poetry. As well as using words to convey meaning, poems use other aspects of language (the sounds and shapes of words and letters) to create effects and make the message memorable. They therefore provide vehicles for investigating how language affects us - and how we can use language to affect others.

USING THE WORKSHEETS

The worksheets form the basis of 28 poetry lessons, covering requirements of the National Literacy Strategy for Year 3 and 4. They are based on the poems in the anthology *Footprints On The Page*, compiled by Fiona Waters and published by Evans Brothers Ltd. The activities are not intended to be used by pupils without teacher support.

Planning
- Use the worksheet to focus your thoughts when preparing a lesson.
- Familiarise yourself with the recommended poems in advance.
- Plan your lesson round the questions on the worksheet, ensuring you cover any technical vocabulary and aspects of appreciation.

Shared work
- Use the poem or poems as shared text for whole class teaching. This will usually be before the children complete the worksheet, although occasionally (Worksheets 2, 6, 7 and 9) parts should be completed in advance.
- Cover comprehension and appreciation of the poem(s) as well as specific linguistic or poetic effects. Ensure children understand any technical terms.
- Prepare children for independent work through plenty of discussion around the questions on the worksheet.

Group work
- Give out the worksheet for completion during independent directed activity time. On the first few occasions, go through the activities with pupils first, discussing and explaining how to complete them.
- Ask all pupils to complete the main part of the worksheet. If the topic has been well prepared, it should be accessible to children at a range of ability levels, and you can differentiate their achievement by outcome.
- Set the 'extension activity' (included on most worksheets and marked with the symbol [symbol]) for more able children to complete unaided.
- Use this also, if wished, as a focus for guided reading/writing with a lower ability group.

Plenary
- Celebrate and discuss successfully completed worksheets during the plenary session.
- Draw attention again to the main teaching points, including any technical terms.

MOVING ON FROM THE WORKSHEETS

As you work through the worksheets, you will be able to draw on children's growing awareness of language and poetical devices when studying other poems in the collection. Help them apply the concepts and technical terminology to develop their enjoyment and appreciation of a widening range of poems.

- Choose poems that relate to other texts studied, or other areas of the curriculum; poems that revise specific aspects of poetry, or ones that the class will find pleasurable or moving.
- Read poems aloud to children before discussion, so they experience rhythm, rhyme and other poetic effects through their ears as well as their eyes.
- Through discussion, develop pupils' basic reading comprehension, e.g. content, characters, setting, and their appreciation of the underlying message of the poem.

- Draw attention to organisational elements like rhyme scheme (see worksheet 4) and use of language to create effects, e.g. rhyme (worksheets 2-7), vocabulary (worksheets 8-10, 12-14), imagery (worksheet 15), alliteration (worksheet 14).
- Follow up reading and discussion with a variety of activities (see below).

PRESENTING POETRY

Once pupils are used to reading poetry, occasionally vary the way you present poems, e.g:
- Display with certain words covered by Blutak or Post-its, for pupils to work them out.
- Cover the title for pupils to invent their own after reading.
- Cut up the poem into verses (or lines - see worksheets 6 and 7) and display at random, for pupils to assemble and compare with the original.

As well as introducing new poems, ensure there are many opportunities to revisit old favourites.
- Begin some shared poetry sessions by re-reading (or asking children to read) a couple of poems shared before.
- Use the plenary session to revisit familiar poems displaying poetic characteristics you have covered that day.
- Organise occasional "Pupils' Choice" sessions, when pupils read or recite chosen poems.
- Create and maintain an illustrated class poetry anthology or Poetry Box. This should contain carefully-made copies of favourite poems studied in class and the best poems written by class members. Browsing in and adding to this collection could be a regular assignment during independent group time.

POETRY FOLLOW-UPS

The worksheets are intended to follow up specific lessons, reminding children of significant aspects of the particular poems studied. However, poetry can inspire a wide variety of creative responses. The following selection of tasks can be set for pupils to follow up poetry in the Literacy Hour or to link it to other areas of the curriculum.

Shared, guided or independent writing
- Use poems as models for own poetry writing (many children's poems in the anthology are particularly appropriate for this).
- Write "sequels" to poems, e.g. the same subject matter from an alternative viewpoint.
- Convert the content of a poem into another genre of writing, e.g. newspaper report, 'Wanted poster', letter, advertisement.

Presentation, drama, movement
- Learn poems by heart for a class recital.
- Prepare choral readings or other types of performance (perhaps with musical accompaniment or sound effects)
- Create performances of poems on tape.
- Dramatise a story poem (as it is read aloud).
- Role-play characters from poems (e.g. choose a character to be in 'the hotseat', staying in role while other pupils interview you).
- Freeze-frame a poem with your group, i.e. choose a selection of moments from a poem to create a sequence of 'freeze frame' tableaux.
- Re-present a poem as a sequence of movements, (individually or in groups) using space, body-shape and varying speeds.

Art, DT, ICT and Music
- Re-present poems through painting, drawing, collage, model-making (e.g. groups choose familiar poems and create re-presentations for other groups to guess).
- Write and illustrate a poem as a poster.
- Design a poster advertising a poem (using colour, shape, images and lines from the poem).
- Add to the class anthology or poetry box.
- Word-process your favourite poem, using different fonts and other effects.
- Create multimedia representations of poems, using words, sound, animation, etc.
- Devise musical accompaniments or sound effects for poems.
- Compose simple tunes to accompany poems with strong rhythm or pattern.

Learning Objectives — Worksheets

Learning Objectives	1	2	3	4	5	6	7	8	9	10	11	12	13	14	15	16	17	18	19	20	21	22	23	24	25	26	27	28
Read aloud and recite poems	▓	▓																									▓	
Recite poems by heart																												
Prepare poems for performance																	▓											
Compare poems on a similar theme			▓																									
Compare poems by one writer							▓																		▓			
Express/discuss responses			▓																									
Justify preferences																					▓					▓		
Identify features of a poet's work																	▓											
Investigate form and language			▓		▓										▓	▓					▓	▓				▓		
Collect/write words and phrases	▓																											
Distinguish rhyme/non-rhyme					▓																							
Recognise rhyme schemes	▓	▓	▓		▓	▓																						
Recognise rhythm, clap syllables									▓							▓							▓					
Recognise uses of repetition																				▓					▓			
Investigate simple forms																												
Compare narrative/descriptive styles																▓	▓											
Understand use of expressive language								▓																			▓	
Experiment with adjectives and verbs																												
Recognise/use figurative language						▓				▓					▓			▓										
Recognise word play for effect							▓	▓	▓										▓	▓		▓						▓
Understand/use simile, metaphor								▓			▓		▓		▓													
Use alliteration, onomatopoeia																												
Explore humorous/nonsense verse																			▓		▓	▓						
Investigate/write shape poems																							▓					
Recognise features of older poetry																												
Find out about a popular poet																								▓				
Write new/extended verses	▓	▓	▓																									
Write on structure/style of poems											▓	▓		▓				▓										
Write poetry to perform					▓																							
Present after revising/refining					▓							▓		▓														

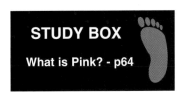
Rhyme

● Read **What is Pink?** by **Christina Rossetti**
● Underline the name of each colour with a pencil of the same colour.
● Now underline each colour's rhyming word with the same colour pencil.

What is Pink?

What is pink? A rose is pink
By the fountain's brink.
What is red? A poppy's red
In its barley bed.
What is blue? The sky is blue
Where the clouds float through.
What is white? A swan is white
Sailing in the light.
What is yellow? Pears are yellow
Rich and ripe and mellow.
What is green? The grass is green,
With small flowers between.
What is violet? Clouds are violet
In the summer twilight.
What is orange? Why, an orange,
Just an orange!

● Make lists of words that rhyme with the names of the colours.

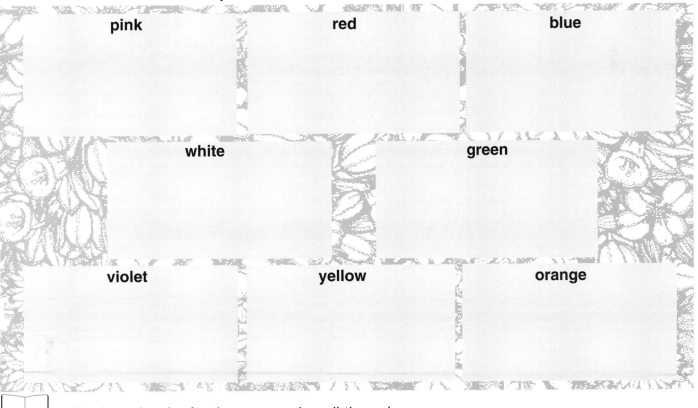

pink	red	blue

white	green

violet	yellow	orange

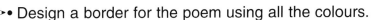

• Design a border for the poem using all the colours.
• Write some new lines for the poem **What is Pink?** using your own ideas and rhyming words.

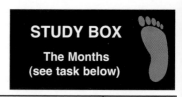

Patterns of rhyme and verse

The Months by **Sara Coleridge** is a classic poem written in rhyming couplets.

● Fill in the spaces and complete the poem with your own words.
● Make sure you keep to the pattern of rhyme and rhythm.

January brings the snow,
Makes our feet and fingers ....

February brings the ....
Thaws the frozen lake again.

March brings breezes loud and shrill,
Stirs the dancing ....

April brings the primrose sweet,
Scatters daisies at our ....

May brings flocks of pretty ....
Skipping by their fleecy dams.

June brings tulips, lilies, ...
Fills the children's hands with posies.

Hot July brings cooling ....
Apricots and gillyflowers.

August brings the sheaves of ....
Then the harvest home is borne.

Warm September brings the fruit,
Sportsmen then begin to ....

Fresh October brings the ....
Then to gather nuts is pleasant.

Dull November brings the blast,
Then the leaves are whirling ....

Chill December brings the ....
Blazing fire, and Christmas treat.

● Use the **Contents** page to find the poem in '**Footprints on the Page**'.
Compare your version with the original.
● Decorate your work by completing the illustrations for each month of the year.

Name . . . . Date . . . .

Rhyming and non-rhyming poetry

● Read and talk about **The Cats of Kilkenny**, a rhyming poem, and **Sleeping Cats** by **Moira Andrew**, a poem that doesn't use rhyme.

The Cats of Kilkenny

Groups of words that rhyme:

_____ _____

_____ _____

Rhyming couplet you like:

_____

_____

Why you like it:

_____

_____

Sleeping Cats

The verse you like best:

_____

_____

_____

Why you like the description:

_____

_____

_____

● Learn by heart the easiest poem.
● Explain why it is easy to learn.

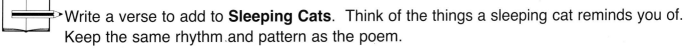

Write a verse to add to **Sleeping Cats**. Think of the things a sleeping cat reminds you of. Keep the same rhythm and pattern as the poem.

Name . . . . Date . . . .

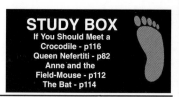
STUDY BOX
If You Should Meet a
Crocodile - p116
Queen Nefertiti - p82
Anne and the
Field-Mouse - p112
The Bat - p114

Different rhyme schemes

● We have used letters to show the rhyme schemes of the two poems.

● Now you can use colours to mark the words that have the same rhyme.

If You Should Meet a Crocodile
Anonymous

If you should meet a Crocodile	A
Don't take a stick and poke him;	B
Ignore the welcome in his smile,	A
Be careful not to stroke him.	B
For as he sleeps upon the Nile,	A
He thinner gets and thinner;	C
And whene'er you meet a Crocodile	A
He's ready for his dinner.	C

Queen Nefertiti
Anonymous

Spin a coin, spin a coin,	A
All fall down;	B
Queen Nefertiti	C
Stalks through the town.	B
Over the pavements	D
Her feet go clack,	E
Her legs are as tall	F
As a chimney stack.	E

● Read **Anne and the Field-Mouse** by **Ian Serraillier**, and **The Bat** by **Theodore Roethke**.

• Write out four lines from each of the poems.
• Mark the pairs of rhyming words with the same colour.
• Use letters to show the rhyming pattern.

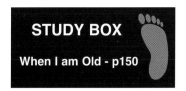

Non-rhyming poetry

● Read and talk about **When I am Old** by **Amelia Clarke**.

How many lines in each verse?

Does it use repetition?

Does it have a rhythm?

Do verses have a pattern?

Is it written in sentences?

Whose **voice** is speaking the poem?

What is the **message** of the poem?

Phrases or sentences I liked	Why I liked them

● Write some phrases of your own using the same pattern.
● Use your work to add another verse to the poem.
● Delete, add or change words until you think it sounds right.

• Rehearse a performance of the poem with your additional lines.
• Collect props to help illustrate the words.

Form and language 1

●   Cut out these lines and arrange them as a verse of poetry.

✂   -

In the broad and fiery street,

· ·

How beautiful is the rain!

· ·

Like the tramp of hoofs!

· ·

After the dust and heat,

· ·

In the narrow lane,

· ·

How it clatters along the roofs,

· ·

How beautiful is the rain!

· ·

●   Read **Rain in Summer** by **Henry Wadsworth Longfellow**, and check your work.

Tick the check list to show how much each clue helped you.
1 is very little help.   5 is really helpful.

	1	2	3	4	5
Rhyme					
Rhythm					
Descriptive style					
Narrative style					
Written in sentences					
Written in phrases					
Uses figurative language					

 • Describe how you used the clues.
      • Write out and cut up the lines of the second verse for your partner to arrange.

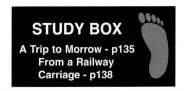
Form and language 2

● Cut out these lines from two poems and arrange them correctly.

✂ -

And there is the green for stringing the daisies!

- -

All by himself and gathering brambles;

- -

I started on a journey just about a week ago

- -

Here is a tramp who stands and gazes;

- -

That Morrow had been ridiculed a century or so.

- -

I never was a traveller and really didn't know

- -

Here is a child who clambers and scrambles,

- -

For the little town of Morrow in the State of Ohio.

- -

● Read the poems and check your work.
● Which poem is descriptive and which is narrative?
● Compare the ways in which they are written. (See Worksheet 6)

A Trip to Morrow
Anonymous

Type of poem:

Structure:

Language:

From a Railway Carriage
R.L.Stevenson

Type of poem:

Structure:

Language:

8

Name . . . . Date . . . .

STUDY BOX
The Dragon Who Ate
Our School - p42
The Witch's Cat - p77
Sea Timeless Song - p125

Patterns with words

●   Write out the repeated words or phrases from each of the poems.

1. **The Dragon Who Ate Our School**
   by **Nick Toczek**

2. **The Witch's Cat**
   by **Ian Serraillier**

3. **Sea Timeless Song**
   by **Grace Nichols**

●   Tick the two most important reasons that repetition is used in each poem.

	Rhythm	Mood	Emphasis	To round off	To fill a gap	Traditional
1						
2						
3						

Find another poem that uses repetition. Why is it used?

9

Name . . . . Date . . . .

STUDY BOX
Imagine - p92
Opening a Packet
of Biscuits - p39
The Hen - p108

Choice of words - verbs

● Fill the space in each line with the best verb you can think of.

Imagine

If the sea . . . . in the sky,

And trees . . . . underground,

And if all the fish . . . . giant teeth,

And all the cows . . . . round;

If birds . . . . backwards all the time,

And vultures . . . . the land.

If bricks . . . . down instead of rain,

If all there was . . . . sand;

If every man . . . . seven heads

And we . . . . Double Dutch,

And if the sun . . . . out at night,

I wouldn't . . . . it much.

● Compare your version with the original poem.

 · Read **Opening a Packet of Biscuits** by **Pat Moon**, and **The Hen** by **Lord Alfred Douglas**.

· Choose one of the poems to write out, removing all the verbs.

· Ask your partner to think of suitable verbs to fill the gaps.

· Compare their work with the original. Which version is better?

10
Name . . . . Date . . . .

STUDY BOX
Tiger in a Zoo - p129
Roger the Dog - p104
Bumblefoot - p103

Choice of words - adjectives and verbs

● Read **Tiger in a Zoo** by **Pat Moon**, and write the three descriptive phrases you liked most and say why you liked them.

Phrase I liked:

Why I liked it:

Phrase I liked:

Why I liked it:

Phrase I liked:

Why I liked it:

• Read **Roger the Dog** by **Ted Hughes**, and **Bumblefoot** by **Colin Thiele**.

• Which poem do you like best and why?
• Choose the two best phrases about what the dog is like and two about what the dog does.
• Write phrases about what another animal is like and what it does.

Playing with language

● Read and talk about **Hands** by **Peter Young**.

● Copy out the words of the poem and decorate the borders with a pattern of hands.

. . . .

. . . .

. . . .

. . . .

. . . .

. . . .

. . . .

. . . .

. . . .

. . . .

. . . .

. . . .

. . . .

. . . .

. . . .

● Track the word *hands* through the poem as it changes and finally becomes *hand*.

● Write the words here. (There are 23 altogether.)

Hands - handling - dangling - . . . .

. . . .

. . . .

. . . .

. . . .

● Choose other words, such as *feet* or *nose*, to change in the same way.

Write a poem about feet or another part of the body in the same style as **Hands**.

Figurative language

- Read **The Fog** by **F.R. McCreary**.
- Brainstorm good words and phrases about another sort of weather, using figurative language.

Type of weather:

Colour words:

**Character or animal
you'd compare it to:**

How it sounds:

How it eats:

What it does to people:

Its effect in towns:

Its effect in the country:

- Look for links between the words and phrases you've chosen -

rhyme

patterns of sound

alliteration

- Use your brainstorm to write your own figurative poem.
- Draft your work.
- Change, trim and extend your lines and phrases until your poem sounds right.

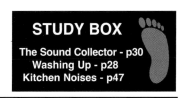
Onomatopoeia

- List the onomatopoeic words in **The Sound Collector** by **Roger McGough**.
- Which object makes each sound?
- Think of onomatopoeic words of your own for each object.

Onomatopoeia from poem	What makes the sound	My onomatopoeic word

- Look for onomatopoeic words in **Washing Up** by **Sarah Gunn**, and **Kitchen Noises** by **Matthew Hinton**.
- Write the words in forms which suggest the sounds.

Name . . . . Date . . . .

Alliteration

- Read **One Old Ox** and choose the three best alliterative lines.
- Write and illustrate the lines.

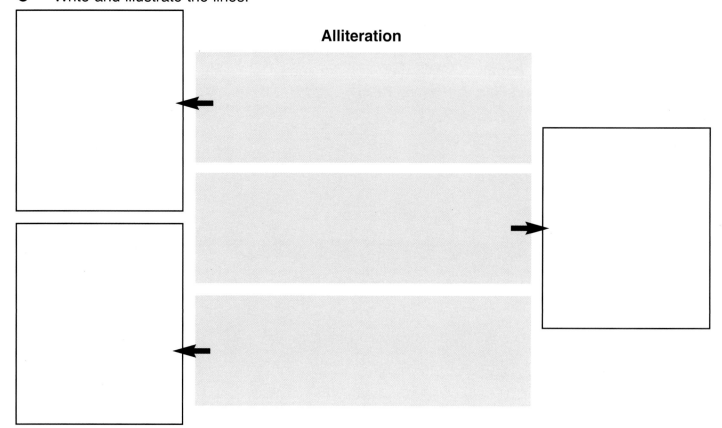

Alliteration

- Write your own alliterative lines on the same pattern.

Number	Adjective	Noun	Verb	Noun
One	old	ox	opening	oysters

- Choose your best lines and draft a poem.
- Alter words until you think the rhythm and sound are right.
- Present your poem and illustrate the border.

Name . . . . Date . . . .

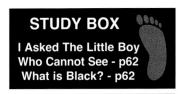
Simile and metaphor

● Read **I Asked The Little Boy Who Cannot See**.
● Copy the similes or metaphors used for each colour and write one of your own.

Simile in poem   **Your simile**

Green

is like...

Red

is like...

Purple

is like...

Yellow

is like...

Metaphor in poem   **Your metaphor**

Blue

is...

White

is...

● Use coloured pencils to make a border for each box.

• Read **What is Black?** by **Mary O'Neil.**
• Choose another colour.
• Write your own poem in the same style.

Name . . . . Date . . . .

Narrative in poetry - phrasing

● Read and talk about **The Witch and the AA Man** by **Barry Buckingham.**
● Write a summary of the story.

● Write each sentence of the first two verses on a separate strip and cut them out.

● Get your partner to paste the sentences together to form the lines of the verses.
These clues will help:

| length of line | rhythm | rhyme | sense of phrases | story line |

● Ask your partner how the different clues helped.
● Compare your partner's work with the original poem.

Name . . . .   Date . . . .

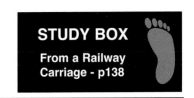
Descriptive poetry - performance

- Organise a performance of **From a Railway Carriage** by **R.L. Stevenson**.
- Each symbol could indicate a different speaker or group of speakers.
- Write out the words of the other verses in the same way.

✳ Faster than fairies,　● faster than witches,

▼ Bridges and houses,　■ hedges and ditches;

✳ ● And charging along like troops in a battle,

▼ ■ All through the meadows the horses and cattle:

✳ All of the sights of the hill and the plain

● Fly as thick as driving rain;

▼ And ever again,　■ in the wink of an eye,

✳ ● ▼ ■ Painted stations whistle by.

. . . .

. . . .

. . . .

. . . .

. . . .

. . . .

. . . .

. . . .

- Repeat lines putting the stress on different words until you find what works best.
- Create the rhythm of a steam train in your reading.
- Devise sound effects using percussion instruments.
- Draw illustrations down the sides of the poem.

18 Name . . . . Date . . . .

Simple forms

●   Read **Two Times Table**.

●   Tap out the rhythm of the poem.

> Twice one are two,
> Violets white and blue

> Twice eleven are twenty-two,
> Daisies wet with morning dew.

●   Write your own version of the three times table in rhyming couplets.
      Keep a steady rap-like rhythm.

Three times one will give you three,   Three times seven give twenty-one,

Three times two will give you six   Three times eight give twenty-four,

Three times three will give you nine,   Three times nine give twenty-seven,

Three times four will give you twelve,   Three times ten will give thirty,

Three times five will give fifteen,   Three times eleven give thirty-three,

Three times six will give eighteen,   Three times twelve give thirty-six,

●   Check your lines for rhyme and rhythm.

      Ask several speakers from your group to read your poem.

      Plan a musical accompaniment.

      Perform your poem as a tables rap.

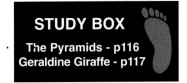

STUDY BOX

The Pyramids - p116
Geraldine Giraffe - p117

Shape poems

- Read the poems and compare them.
- Complete the checklist. ✔ for yes ✗ for no

- Write shape poems in these two shapes.

	The Pyramids by Mike Jubb	Geraldine Giraffe by Colin West
Uses rhythm		
Uses rhyme		
Written in verses		
Uses figurative language		
Humorous		
Shape suited to subject		

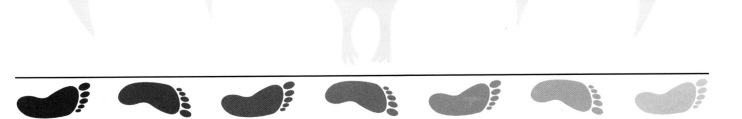

STUDY BOX
The Electronic
House - p26
Words I Like - p53
Socks - p56

Lists

- Read **The Electronic House** by **Wes Magee**, **Words I Like** by **Steve Turner**, and **Socks** by **Colin West**.
- Compare the poems. ✔ for yes ✗ for no

	The Electronic House	Words I like	Socks
Written in verses			
Uses rhyme			
Definite rhythm			
Meaning more important than sound			
Sound more important than meaning			
Lists of single words			
Lists of phrases			

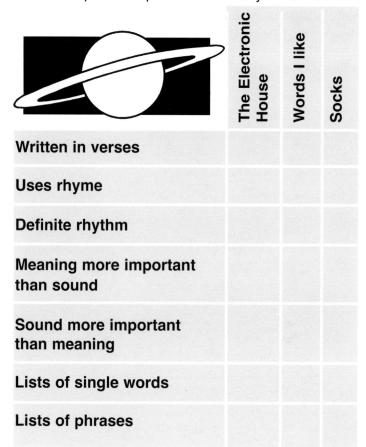

- Choose one poem.
- Turn it into a performance.
- Use different voices.
- Plan sound effects.

- Make your own lists.

Words I like	Words that rhyme	Words that alliterate

21

Name . . . . Date . . . .

STUDY BOX
I'd Like to be a Teabag - p36
I've Never Heard the Queen
Sneeze - p88
St George and
the Dragon - p90

Humorous poetry

● Read **I'd Like to be a Teabag** by **Peter Dixon**, **I've Never Heard the Queen Sneeze** by **Brian Patten**, and **St George and the Dragon** by **Finola Akister**.

I'd like to be a Teabag by Peter Dixon

Funniest phrases:

Why they amused me:

I've Never Heard the Queen Sneeze by Brian Patten

TISSUES

Funniest phrases:

Why they amused me:

St George and the Dragon by Finola Akister

Funniest phrases:

Why they amused me:

Choose your favourite humorous poem from the book and practise it to present to the class.

Name . . . . Date . . . .

STUDY BOX
The Spangled
Pandemonium - p94
When Fishes Set
Umbrellas Up - p96
The Quangle Wangle's Hat - p97

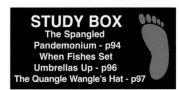

Nonsense verse

● Read **The Spangled Pandemonium** by **Palmer Brown**, **When Fishes Set Umbrellas Up** by **Christina Rossetti**, and **The Quangle Wangle's Hat** by **Edward Lear**.

● Copy phrases you liked and explain why you liked them.

Alliteration:	**Onomatopoeia:**

Invented words:	**Fantastic creatures:**

Rhyming phrases:	**Amusing ideas:**

● On the back of this sheet, draw a picture of a scene from the poem you liked best.
  Title of poem: _____

Classic poetry

- **Thomas Campbell** lived from 1777 to 1844.
- Read and talk about **The Parrot**.

The structure of the poem
Number of verses:

Number of lines in verses:

Rhyme scheme:
(See Worksheet 4)

The language of the poem
Old-fashioned words:

Unusual phrases:

Unusual order:

- One verse sums up the message of the poem. Which is it? Write it here.

_____

_____

_____

_____

- Write the message of the poem in your own words on the back of this sheet.

Name . . . . Date . . . .

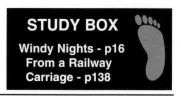

A popular poet - Robert Louis Stevenson

● Robert Louis Stevenson lived from 1850 to 1894. He was born in Edinburgh and had to spend long spells of his childhood in bed because he was not strong. His mother and his nurse amused him by telling him stories and reciting poems and hymns. His father was a civil engineer and Robert went with him on long journeys by train to inspect lighthouses around the rugged coasts of Scotland. When he was older he travelled abroad for the sake of his health. Eventually he made his home, with his wife and stepchildren, in one of the Samoan Islands in the South Pacific. The natives loved Robert Louis Stevenson and gave him the title 'Tusitala' - teller of tales. When he died they carried his body to the summit of a mountain where he was buried with a verse of his own as an epitaph.

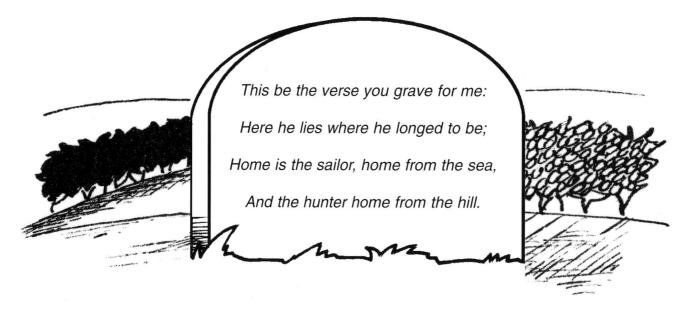

This be the verse you grave for me:

Here he lies where he longed to be;

Home is the sailor, home from the sea,

And the hunter home from the hill.

● Find out more about **Robert Louis Stevenson**:

The titles of some of his best children's poems:

_____

_____

_____

The name of the anthology of his children's poems:

_____

The names of two of his best-known novels:

_____

_____

➤Read **Windy Nights** and **From a Railway Carriage**.

Name . . . . Date . . . .

STUDY BOX
Looking Down on Roofs - p24
The Wraggle Taggle Gipsies - p24

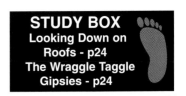

Comparing poems on a similar theme 1

- Read and talk about the two poems, then compare them and fill in the grid.

		A modern poem **Looking Down on Roofs** by **Marian Lines**	*A traditional poem* **The Wraggle Taggle Gipsies**
How the poem is written	**Number of verses**		
	Number of lines per verse		
	Repeated lines and phrases		
	Words that show the poem is ● **modern** ● **traditional**		
The message of the poem	**Whose point of view?**		
	What is the point of view of the poem?		
	What are the gains of the new home?		
	What are the 'losses'?		

- Which poem do you like best?
- Use the information in your grid and write about the poem on the back of the sheet.
- Explain why you like one poem more than the other.

Comparing poems on a similar theme 2

●   Read these two poems on the theme of pollution, then fill in the grid.

		The Walk by **Michelle Walker**	**Mummy, Oh Mummy** Anon
How the poem is written	Number of verses		
	Number of lines in verses		
	Repeated lines and phrases		
The message of the poem	Whose voices are heard?		
	What is the message of each voice?		
	The sorts of pollution which are mentioned		
	Who is to blame?		

- Sum up the message of each poem.
- Which poem gives the strongest message about pollution?
- Give your reasons.

Name . . . . Date . . . .

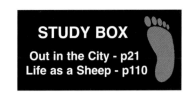
STUDY BOX
Out in the City - p21
Life as a Sheep - p110

Comparing poems by one writer 1

● Read the two poems by **Gareth Owen** and talk about them.

Out in the City

Words that help to create the scene:

_____

Movement words:

_____

Pace of the poem:

_____

Whose voice is heard?

_____

What sort of character is he/she?

_____
_____

Life as a Sheep

Words that help to create the scene:

_____

Movement words:

_____

Pace of the poem:

_____

Whose voice is heard?

_____

What sort of character is he/she?

_____

• Find two more poems by **Gareth Owen**.
• Read and talk about them.
• Compare them in the same way.

Name . . . . Date . . . .

STUDY BOX
Break Dance - p46
I Like - p76
Sea Timeless
Song - p125

Comparing poems by one writer 2

●   Read and talk about these poems by **Grace Nichols**. What is the main message of each poem?

Break Dance

_____

_____

_____

_____

_____

_____

_____

I Like

_____

_____

_____

_____

_____

_____

_____

Sea Timeless Song

_____

_____

_____

_____

_____

_____

_____

●   Choose a different colour to suit the mood of each poem.
     Design coloured borders round your work about the poems.

  • Which poem did you like best and why?
    • In what ways is it like the others? In what ways is it different?